At Home in Harmony

Bringing Families and Communities Together in Song

by

Meg Chittenden

Waldorf
PUBLICATIONS
RESEARCH INSTITUTE FOR Waldorf EDUCATION

Printed with support from the Waldorf Curriculum Fund

Published by:

Waldorf Publications at the
Research Institute for Waldorf Education
38 Main Street
Chatham, NY 12037

Title: *At Home in Harmony*:
   Bringing Families and Communities Together in Song
Author: Meg Chittenden
Layout and Illustrations: Meg Chittenden
Proofreading: Ruth Reigal

Table of Contents

Song Descriptions and Sheet Music

Dear Singers,

Thank you for picking up *At Home in Harmony*. Singing is a uniquely human act. It is our birthright to lift up our voices in song. When we sing, we transform the spaces around us and within us. When we sing together in harmony, we listen closely, tuning in to one another while also staying true to our own voices. In so doing, we manifest the beauty that arises out of embracing differences while recognizing ourselves as part of a common, human song. That's why, for me, singing in harmony is a form of putting peace into practice.

Yet, over the past few centuries, the emphasis in Western music has shifted from participation by many to performance by a few. While it's rare to find a person who doesn't enjoy music, it's almost as rare these days for a person to feel welcome to join in the joy of music-making. This book is intended to serve as a gentle hand reaching out and inviting you to take your place in the choir. You don't need a certain kind of voice or any special training. All you need is some air in your lungs and the courage to open your mouth and let the tone flow freely through you. Whether you are an experienced singer or new to harmony, someone looking for songs to sing around the fire with friends, or a parent or teacher seeking to bring more singing into your days with the children in your care, there is something in this collection for you.

Whatever brings you to it, I hope this book will bring you a new or renewed sense of the power and potential of your own voice. I hope these songs become pathways through which you, and those with whom you share them, are able to experience the joy and connection inherent in harmony singing. And I hope that, by sharing harmony with our friends, family, children, and community, more of us are able to reclaim our right to sing.

HOW TO USE THIS BOOK

In this book, you will find a selection of songs arranged to be sung in harmony. Some are rounds. Most are songs with multiple parts. They are primarily folksongs from various parts of the world. The offerings begin with songs to greet the day, move through songs to accompany work and play, and conclude with selections that welcome the coming night. All are songs that I have sung and enjoyed for years with my own family, school, and community. While adding the harmonies is wonderful, singing the melodies in unison is lovely, too, and is the most appropriate approach for singing with children under the age of nine. (Please see "A Note to Parents and Teachers" on page 9.)

As a first step in exploring this collection, I suggest listening through the "At Home in Harmony" CD to see what songs appeal to you and might lend themselves best to the contexts in which you sing. When you've selected a song you'd like to learn, you have two options. You can simply use the sheet music to learn the parts, teach, and sing them. Or, if sheet music is not your thing and you would benefit from additional support, read on…

LISTEN TO LEARN

By purchasing this book, you have earned yourself access to nine hours of clear, step-by-step instruction to help you learn and teach the songs in this collection and their accompanying harmonies. Every voice part for every song has its own Learning Track that guides you towards learning to sing it with confidence. At the conclusion of each Learning Track, you have the chance to sing the whole song through while the other voice parts play softly in the background. Like new friends, these songs can take time to get to know. Don't expect to master them immediately. The Learning Tracks allow you to go at your own pace, repeating sections as many times as needed or skipping ahead if you'd rather. Just like true friends, if you invest yourself in them, they have the potential to enrich your life for years to come.

To download the Learning Tracks, visit www.singwaldorf.com and click on "My Harmony." You can choose to download one song at a time or the whole bundle all at once. Your purchaser code is: 1MC2PK4HJ7. This code will enable you, as a purchaser of this book, free access to all of the downloads. Please do not copy or share this code.

Your voice, every voice, is a gift the world is waiting to receive. Happy singing!

~Meg

Preface

Andrea Lyman, President
The Association for Waldorf Music Education (AWME)
www. waldorfmusic.org

In these modern times, families and friends so rarely, if at all, gather together to sing, play and be together without the added paraphernalia of televisions, cell phones, video games, or other external devices. In days gone by, when these things were not yet part of our culture, folks would gather together and tell stories, sing songs, play games, and spend their time together in simple, meaningful recreation. People of all ages enjoyed these frequent get-togethers to reconnect, share their lives, and create something together as a community, and music was almost always part of this scenario.

Nowadays, most people take a more passive role in their musical experiences, and relatively few actually make their own music. Many children, in fact, have never heard a live musician play or sing—even their own parents! Increasingly, there is a culturally held idea that only a select few have the talent to make music—the rest of us just listen to others whom we perceive as having something we do not. But music is our human birthright! It is tragic that so many have foregone the simple pleasure of singing or making music because they see themselves as incapable of doing so. It is time to reclaim this birthright by finding the courage to sing with joyful authenticity and to rekindle the enthusiasm of making music with others.

In Waldorf education, the curriculum is rich with music, art, movement, and many types of handwork. These exist not to round out the students' experience, but to acknowledge that we are whole human beings, made up of many facets. Each of these facets is essential, each worthy of educating, nourishing, and cultivating toward the full actualization of ourselves.

Families are at the heart of Waldorf education. Seasonal festivals and other activities are shared by the whole school community, and music-making together is always to be found as an integral part of these gatherings. Music shared by children, faculty, and families invites something that so rarely takes place anymore—a sense of truly sharing our lives with one another as we blend our voices.

Outside of the school setting, however, we find fewer and fewer opportunities to join together in song with family and friends. The simple songs that were once common in most any childhood are being forgotten, and the sense of a family treasury of musical traditions seems to have fallen away. This book serves to provide songs and suggestions to re-enliven this experience.

The Waldorf music pedagogy has its own specific trajectory, with the appropriate use of music at the right stage of the child's development throughout the music curriculum. Traditional and/or more complex harmonies are challenging for the younger child, and in Waldorf music education, these are healthfully presented at a very particular time in the child's stage of development. But there is no reason not to include everyone in making music together—there is always something that anyone and everyone can contribute within the bounds of their own abilities and comfort level. Also, never underestimate the importance of a child's simply listening to others sing. For children, listening can be as active as you or I consider singing aloud to be. They take in the whole experience, and one day they too are singing along with a happy heart.

Carefully selected to bring meaningful musical experiences together with family and friends, the volume you now hold in your hand has been lovingly put together with care and consciousness that will bring many hours of enjoyment to those who recognize the importance of singing together. Created to encourage the active music-making that has greatly diminished in our modern culture, this songbook invites and cultivates the community-building so many of us crave. The very definition of harmony includes the idea of varied parts coming together in a way that complement each other, making the whole greater than the parts. *At Home in Harmony* serves to bring not only satisfying musical experiences to family and community, but it acknowledges that when we join together in a harmonious way, it has the power to transform.

Learn (or recall) a couple of songs, raise your voices together, and delight in the deepening of human relationships through a communal experience of joyful music-making. You, your family, your community, and the whole world will be the better for it!

A Note to Parents and Teachers

If you are a teacher or parent planning to bring these songs to the children in your care, here are some considerations and suggestions you may find useful:

(1) The recordings that accompany this songbook are designed to help you learn the songs so you can bring them, enlivened by your own voice and care, to the children with whom you sing. The recordings are not intended to serve as instruction for children.

(2) The offerings in this collection are geared toward individuals ages nine and up. While many of the melodies, sung in unison, are perfectly lovely for younger children, there is a wealth of Waldorf resources that feature songs selected specifically to nourish children under age nine. Please see the "Resources" section at the end of this book for recommendations.

(3) Please read the section entitled "The Privilege of Song" (page 11) before sharing these songs with your children.

TEACHING SUGGESTIONS

There are innumerable wonderful ways to bring songs to children. Here are a few of the approaches and considerations that I have found beneficial in my teaching:

Particularly with young children, I love to introduce a song through story. This can be as simple as telling the story of the song in prose before singing it. Or you can make up a story that sets the scene in which the song can unfold. An example is offered along with the song "Little Red Bird."

All of these songs offer the opportunity to layer in complexity over time. With younger children, I like to introduce a song in its simplest form. Then, over the course of several weeks, months, or even years, new elements—such as additional harmonies and body percussion—can further enrich the experience of the already familiar song.

When introducing a round, I take plenty of time to get to know the song well before trying it out in parts. I often won't even mention that a song can be sung as a round until we've enjoyed it thoroughly in unison. Just when your children have come to know a song so well that they can sing it without even thinking about it, that is the perfect time to introduce the element of the round. By then, you should already be certain that each group that will carry a part can sing the whole song alone. I find it is always better to sing a round with fewer parts and greater accuracy than the opposite. This allows the harmonies to truly ring out.

With middle school-aged children and up, I find that getting right into harmony is the most satisfying. I usually choose a short section of the song, either the first phrase, the final phrase, or the refrain, and teach all the harmony parts for just that section. My goal is to sing at least one phrase of the song in full harmony before the end of the first session. This sense of the heart of a song draws the singers in and creates momentum for learning the rest. From there, whether we're moving from the beginning to the end or the reverse, we continue to flesh out the song phrase by phrase in full harmony.

When introducing body percussion, I usually teach the song separately. There is a certain kind of magic that arises when you realize that two things you previously thought unrelated are actually inherently connected. Isn't so much of life interwoven in ways that might not at first glance be apparent to us? If you work on the song and the body percussion independently and only when both are mastered disclose that they belong together, you offer your students the affirming experience of hidden connectivity revealed.

My hope is that this project will help you bring more harmony singing into your days with the children in your care. If you run into difficulty or have questions about the songs, please feel free to contact me. The best way to reach me is via email at meg@singwaldorf.com.

The Privilege of Song

This collection includes songs from cultures other than my own. They are songs of celebration and joy and, in some cases, songs born out of profound suffering and struggle. Most of these songs have been sung across generations. I view the presence of these songs in my life as a privilege, not a right. In singing and sharing them, I see both potential for good and potential for harm.

As a teacher, I want to invite children to explore the expanses and plumb the depths of their own humanity as it connects inherently with humanity as a whole. Part of this journey includes exploring what it has meant to be human over the course of history and in many different cultural and geographical contexts. Ideally, the arc of a child's education brings her myriad opportunities to do this thoroughly and thoughtfully. Song can be one pathway that supports and enhances this exploration. Singing gives us the chance to feel with our breath and bones the words and melodies that have arisen out of a multitude of human experiences. In this sense, singing can be one way we tap into a deeper connection with the universal nature of humanity.

At the same time, performing, teaching, or otherwise adopting songs from a culture that is not our own can cause harm. In a context such as the present-day United States, white culture is the dominant culture, meaning it holds the most economic and political power, and its language, values, social customs, and religions are the most widespread and influential in society. It is in this context that other cultures, mostly those associated with brown skin, continue to experience racism in the forms of prejudice, violence, social and economic inequality, and even systemic oppression. Given this reality, when a white person adopts a song from a group oppressed by the dominant culture, this can manifest as yet another form of exploitation. This causes overt harm to individuals and groups experiencing the exploitation as well as latent harm to the unwitting perpetrators. For this reason, how and why we adopt songs from other cultures deserves careful consideration. These concepts may be new or otherwise unclear to you. If so, consider reading about white privilege and cultural appropriation. Some suggested texts are offered below, and many relevant articles can be found on the internet.

I wish there were a perfectly clear way to identify and uphold the good and always avoid harm, but with considerations as complex, multi-dimensional, global, and yet also individual as these, I believe the best we can strive for is generating the most good while causing the least harm. While I don't believe there is a single road map or rule book that people can follow to navigate the shifting landscape of equity, inclusion, and cultural appropriation without ever getting lost, I strive to cultivate in myself an inner compass that seeks ever to align itself with justice. This means my compass needle is continually shifting and realigning as my consciousness evolves and I encounter various unique situations and individuals.

In presenting you with this book, I feel it is critically important that I also offer you some of the considerations that currently guide my sharing of songs. This is not a check-list that allows me to categorize each song as "ok to share" or not. Rather, I see the process of grappling with these considerations as an essential practice toward becoming ever more sensitive, responsive, and just.

What is the relationship, both current and historical, between my culture of origin and the culture out of which this song arose? It would be wonderful if we lived in a world that was truly equitable for all people. Given the realities of institutionalized oppression and systemic racism in the United States, I feel that it is inherently different for me, a white person living in a white-dominant culture, to choose to sing an African-American spiritual than it would be for my brown-skinned neighbor to choose to sing an English folksong. I don't believe that white people should never sing spirituals (as evidenced by my inclusion of two songs from the Georgia Sea Islands in this collection). But I do believe that when a person from a dominant group adopts a song from a less privileged group, it must be done with utmost thoughtfulness and care. Just as important, one must be truly willing to receive and be responsive to any critical feedback that may arise, engaging out of a sense of humility and an eagerness to learn.

What did/does this song mean to the person/people who first sang it? In preparing songs to share, I learn as much as I can about a song's origin and its original significance. How sacred is this song to its culture of origin? For example, some songs have special religious or sacred significance and are intended to be sung only within a certain context or by a person who holds a specific role or status within the song's culture of origin. I will not take up such a song. When I do feel it is appropriate to take up a song myself, I offer all that I can about its origin and meaning. With many traditional folksongs, a general picture is the most I can ascertain, and so I try to be clear about what I don't know as well. While I might also share what a song from another culture has come to mean to me, I try to emphasize that the song is not mine, and I attribute it to its true source(s).

How did I come to know this song? I value human-driven exchange. Therefore, I prioritize sharing songs that I've learned directly from another person who had a culturally significant relationship with the song. Likewise, throughout this project, I have sought to present the material to you as personally as possible. This includes choosing songs with which I feel a strong connection, sharing my experiences with the songs and, through the Learning Tracks, offering the most human instruction I can manage without showing up in your living room.

How can I most authentically present this song? This is one of the most essential considerations for me in teaching or otherwise sharing a song. By this, I do not necessarily mean I aim for accuracy. Sometimes, in an effort to be accurate, we slip into parody, acting out the song as if we were someone else. If you're not sure how this could be offensive, picture a group of white people pretending to be Native American as they sing. To me, that is different from simply singing a song from an indigenous American source. In sharing a song from a culture other than my own, I think it is imperative to recognize that it is literally impossible for me to present it accurately; to imply otherwise would be a grave error. Instead, I strive to sing songs with reverence out of my own experience while acknowledging both inwardly and outwardly the limitations inherent in singing a song arising from a culture other than my own.

What are the limitations of sharing this song? While music and song can be powerful forces for change, it is important to remember that simply singing a song from another culture is not a significant act towards equity. Though it can be easy to mistake one for the other, multicultural repertoire and real equity and inclusion are only distantly related. The former is ideally one (relatively superficial) manifestation of the latter. Too often, we interpret the presence of diversity in song selection (and other areas of curriculum) as evidence of the presence of equity. I hope the considerations discussed above have begun to illuminate that multiculturalism for its own sake can be an unintentional force in opposition to equity. In fact, what is needed is a much more comprehensive shift in perception and practice.

I know that these considerations may seem dauntingly complex. I hope that, if they are new to you, you receive them as an invitation to further thinking, conversation, and learning. I am committed to making myself available to you, should you have an interest in on-going dialogue around these questions or have comments or feedback. The best way to reach me is at meg@singwaldorf.com.

While I see value in singing songs that arise out of the great and beautiful diversity of the human experience, the primary quality I look for in the songs I choose to share with others is a sense of enduring resonance. Whether the song is playful or poignant, light or weighty, simple or complex, all the songs I offer here have lit up some corner of my own humanity, and I hope they will do the same for you.

RECOMMENDED RESOURCES

The Ethics of Cultural Appropriation by James O. Young and Conrad G. Brunk (eds.), Hoboken, NJ: Wiley-Blackwell, 2012.

White Like Me: Reflections on Race from a Privileged Son by Tim Wise, Berkeley, CA: Soft Skull Press, 2011.

Song Descriptions
and
Sheet Music

1. Bright Morning Star

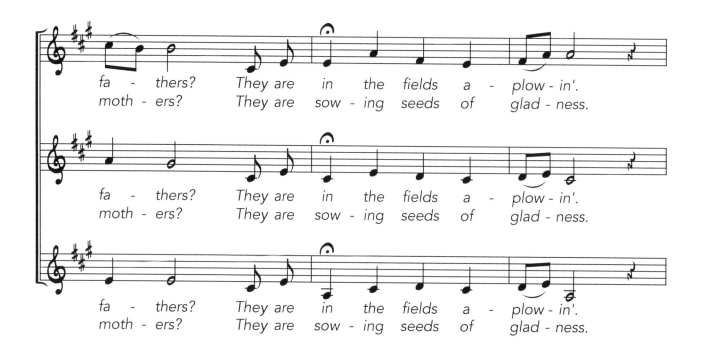

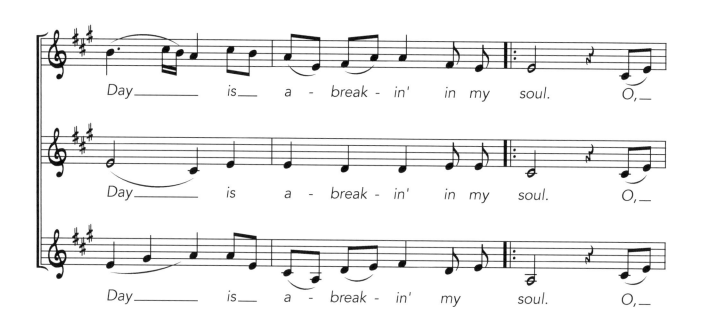

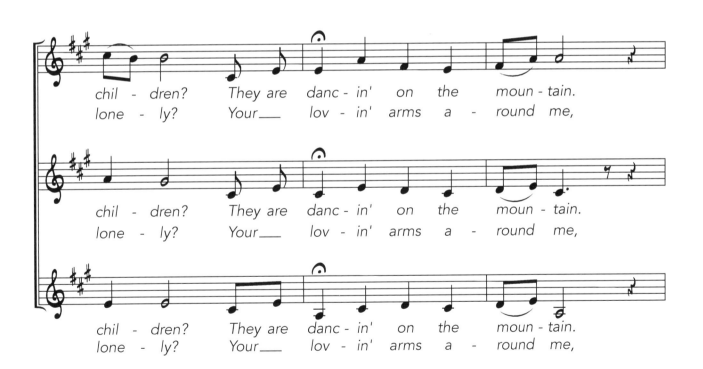

bright morn-ing star a-ris - ing. Day is a - break-in' in my soul.

morn - ing star a-ris - ing. Day___ is a - break-in' in my soul.

morn - ing star a - ris - ing. Day___ is a - break-in' in my soul.

morn - ing star a - ris - ing. Day___ is a - break-in' in my soul.

"Bright Morning Star" has long been a favorite in American folksong circles. Widely believed to have arisen out of southern Appalachia, it has been recorded by the likes of Ruth Crawford Seeger, Judy Collins, the Stanley Brothers, and more recently, Wailin' Jennys and Gillian Welch. One of the beauties of folk music is that it lends itself to adaptation, and there are many versions of this song. I first learned it as a member of the All Souls Unitarian Universalist Church choir in Washington, D.C., and have since adapted the lyrics and arrangement. Perhaps you'll want to add verses or adjust the lyrics to reflect what is most meaningful for you and your family or community.

The harmonies offered here are a bit more complex than others in this collection. If harmony singing is new to you, the melody is wonderful sung in unison. Likewise, if you are singing with young children, I'd encourage you to stick with enjoying the melody together for now, as the harmonies are most appropriate for children nearing adolescence. However you approach this song, I hope that the underlying message of transcendence, renewal, and connection shines through for you.

2. Yonder Come Day

Yon - der come day, oh yon - der come day!

Yon - der come day, oh yon - der come day!

Yon - der come day, oh yon - der come day!

3. Yonder come day. Good morning, day!
   Yonder come day. Good morning, day!
   Yonder come day. Good morning day!
   Yonder come day, day is a-breakin'
      in my soul.

4. Yonder come day, oh, come on, child
   Yonder come day, oh, come on, child
   Yonder come day, oh, come on, child
   Yonder come day, day is a-breakin'
      in my soul.

5. Yonder come day, it's a brand new day
   Yonder come day, it's a brand new day
   Yonder come day, it's a brand new day
   Yonder come day, day is a-breakin'
      in my soul.

24

"Yonder Come Day" comes from the musical tradition of the Georgia Sea Islands, a group of islands off the coast of Southeastern United States. The relative isolation of these islands from the mainland enabled people enslaved on plantations there and their descendants to retain elements of their cultures of origin. A blending of these primarily West African influences with one another and with imposed European influences resulted in a unique culture and language known as Gullah. Gullah continues to thrive to this day, despite the pressures of increasing land development in the area.

While I learned a different arrangement of this song years ago from family members, this version is based on Alan Lomax's recording of Bessie Jones. A member of the Georgia Sea Island Singers, Jones was passionate about the preservation of Gullah music, language, and culture. Many of the songs she sang were taught to her by her African-born grandfather.

Like the African singing styles that spawned it, "Yonder Come Day" was traditionally probably never sung quite the same way twice. I encourage you to make up your own verses and harmonies and add clapping, stomping, and other body percussion. The harmonies offered here are most appropriate for children ages ten and up.

This is a wonderful song to sing in the morning, as the light begins to return after the winter solstice or in times of struggle as a reminder that out of darkness, a new day is born.

3. Country Life

VERSES (sung by Tenor part)

1. Sum - mer when the sun is hot, we sing and we dance and we play a lot. We
2. Au - tumn when the oak trees turn, we gath - er all the wood that's fit to burn. We
3. Win - ter when the sky is gray, we hedge and we ditch our time a - way. But in
4. Spring we sow at the har-vest mow. And that's how the sea - sons round they go. But of

spend all day in work and play and go ram-blin' in the new - mown hay.

cut and we stash and we stow a-way and go ram-blin' in the new - mown hay.

sum - mer when the sun shines gay, we go ram-blin' in the new - mown hay.

all the times, if choose I may, I'd be ram-blin' in the new - mown hay.

"Country Life" is a traditional English folksong that celebrates the beauty and freedom of pastoral living. It has become relatively well-known, thanks to renditions by the Watersons and Eliza Carthy. Because it provides a picture of each season, it can be a wonderful song to revisit throughout the year, adding verses accordingly. Children as young as eight or nine enjoy singing it in unison, and accompanying movements are always welcome. The harmonies can be added into the chorus with older children and adults ready to take on more of a challenge.

4. The Cuckoo Song

Traditional English

A - wake, a - wake, ye dream - ers, the cuck - oo loud - ly calls. The sun shines on the mead - ow and on the moun-tain walls. A - wak - en, a- wak - en, the cuck-oo loud - ly calls. A - wak - en, a - wak - en, the cuck-oo loud - ly calls. Cuck - oo, Cuck - oo, Cuck - oo, Cuck- oo. Cuck- oo, Cuck - oo, Cuck - oo, Cuck - oo.

"The Cuckoo Song" is a traditional German folksong welcoming the coming of day. This song can be sung in unison with younger children and becomes a well-loved and rousing round for ages nine and up. You can play with the tempo and dynamics, going faster or slower and alternating between loud and soft as you wish.

5. Bird Song

Heather Masse

as the morn-ing breaks.____ I hear a

as the morn-ing breaks.____ I hear a bird__ chirp-ing,

as the morn-ing breaks.____

bird__ chirp-ing, up in the sky.____ I'd like to

up in the sky. I'd like to be free like that,

I hear a bird__ chirp-ing, up in the sky.

be free like that, spread my wings so high.____ I see the

spread my wings so high. I see the riv-er flow-ing,

I'd like to be free like that, spread my wings so high.

"Bird Song" is an original composition by Heather Masse of Wailin' Jennys, and it is offered here with her generous permission. Children always seem to be drawn to the timeless poetic imagery and enchanting melody of this song. In my teaching, I often introduce it in two-part harmony with ten-year-old children (Grade 5) and then add the third, lower harmony in subsequent years as a way of revisiting and enriching an already well-loved song. The experience is akin to the delight of discovering something new and wonderful about a friend who is already dear to us.

6. We Love Our Children

"We Love Our Children" is an original composition by the Kanenhi:io Singers (pronounced Ganaheo and meaning "the Good Seeds" in the Mohawk language). The women of this group live in the Wahta Mohawk Territory of Ontario, Canada, and represent many First Nation peoples, including the Mohawk, Innu, Potawatomi, and Cree nations.

Combining traditional rhythms and influences with original lyrics and harmonies, this song is sung in the Mohawk language. It urges all people to love their children, as they are the future of the world. The group's lead singer, Watahine (The One Who Walks Beside the Path), heard this song in a dream when she was pregnant with her son. I am very grateful to Watahine and the Kanenhi:io Singers for granting me permission to share this beautiful song with you.

7. Olélé

Traditional Congolese

O lé lé, O lé lé mo-li-ba ma-ka-see

O lé lé, O lé lé mo-li-ba ma-ka-see

O lé lé, O lé lé mo-li-ba ma-ka-see

Bo-kah na-yeh, bo-kah na-yeh bo-kah bo-kah ka sa ee.

Bo-kah na-yeh, bo-kah na-yeh bo-kah bo-kah ka sa ee.

Bo-kah na-yeh, bo-kah na-yeh bo-kah bo-kah ka sa ee.

Bo-kah na-yeh, bo-kah na-yeh bo-kah bo-kah ka sa ee.

Bo-kah na-yeh, bo-kah na-yeh bo-kah bo-kah ka sa ee.

Bo-kah na-yeh, bo-kah na-yeh bo-kah bo-kah ka sa ee.

"Olélé" is a traditional Uélé River rowing song from the Democratic Republic of the Congo. The rhythm provides a steady pulse to help synchronize rowing, though this song is also sometimes sung as a lullaby. The Lingala lyrics translate to: "Oh, the current is very strong. Row! Row! His country is the Kasai" (a river in southwestern DRC).

This song came to me from a fellow music teacher many years ago. I often bring it as a way of beginning to explore harmony with children around the age of nine or ten. You can add in movement by experimenting with stepping on the down beat (the first beat of every measure) and then switching to marking every beat. To explore the contrast between rhythm and beat, you can add in clapping on the rhythm while stepping on the beat. This also provides a kinesthetic experience of a triplet.

8. Little Bitty Man

Like many of my favorite songs, I learned "Little Bitty Man" from my aunt, Carol Kelly, an experienced Waldorf school teacher who has also taught music for Antioch University's Waldorf teacher training for many years.

Rooted in the American Deep South, "Little Bitty Man" is sung by Mary McDonald on Alan Lomax's *Deep River of Song* collection, *Alabama: From Lullabies to Blues*. Though originally a single-part lullaby, it is wonderful when sung as a round as well. I offer it here in four parts, appropriate for ages nine and up. Gestures and movement are welcome additions.

9. Acitrón

Traditional Mexican

High harmony

A-cit-rón de un fan-dan-go, San-go, San-go, Sa-ba-ré, Sa-ba-

Melody

A-cit-rón de un fan-dan-go, San-go, San-go, Sa-ba-ré, Sa-ba-

Low harmony

A-cit-rón de un fan-dan-go, San-go, San-go, Sa-ba-ré, Sa-ba-

ré que va pa-san-do con su tri-ki, tri-ki tran.

ré que va pa-san-do con su tri-ki, tri-ki tran.

ré que va pa-san-do con su tri-ki, tri-ki tran.

"Acitrón" is a lively Mexican singing game. The whimsical lyrics are mostly in Spanish, but some are said to have roots in Bantu. Loosely translated, the song means: "A cactus (acitrón) in the circle dance (Fandango). Sabaré comes passing by, playing "triki triki tran" (the sound of his strumming)." In some versions, Sabaré is singing (cantando) instead of passing (passando).

To play the game, singers sit in a circle, each with a stone, cup, or other small object in front of them. As they sing, the singers pick up the stone and place it in front of the neighbor to their right on the downbeat. In this way, the stones are passed around the circle. At "triki triki tran," instead of passing the stone, each singer taps the stone on the ground three times, first reaching across to tap in front of their neighbor on the right, then back to the place where they picked up the stone, and then across again. Only on the third tap, which coincides with singing "tran," does each singer drop that stone in front of the neighbor, and the passing resumes as before. Though it can be played as an elimination game, I prefer to have a shared goal of seeing how many song cycles the group can accomplish together. This song works best with ages nine and up and is wonderful whether sung in unison or with the accompanying harmonies.

10. O Mama Bakudala

Woh ma-ma ba-ku-da-la ba-be than - da-za.

(Woh ma-ma ba-ku-da-la ba-be than - da-za.)

(Woh ma-ma ba-ku-da-la ba-be than - da-za.)

Woh ma-ma ba-ku-da-la ba-be than - da-za.

Woh ma-ma ba-ku-da-la ba-be than - da-za.

Woh ma-ma ba-ku-da-la ba-be than - da-za.

Ba - be than - da-za, ba-be than - da-za.

Ba - be than - da-za, ba-be than - da-za.

Ba - be than - da-za, ba-be than - da-za.

Ba - be than - da - za, ba - be than - da - za. Sin

Ba - be than - da - za, ba - be than - da - za.

Ba - be than - da - za, ba - be than - da - za.

Ba - be than - da - za, ba - be than - da - za.

Ba - be than - da - za, ba - be than - da - za.

Ba - be than - da - za, ba - be than - da - za.

"O Mama Bakudala" has been with me long enough that I no longer remember our first encounter. Its origins are South African, and I have seen it attributed to both Zulu and Xhosa sources. These languages are so closely related, it's possible that versions of the song exist in both. The translation I believe to be most accurate is:

> Women of the past used to pray.
> They were praying, they were praying.
> We are like this, like this, like this because of prayer,
> Because of prayer, because of prayer.

For me, this song carries both a sense of gratitude for those who have come before and a reminder that the clarity and integrity of our intentions determines who we are. Because of the call-and-response format and the layering of simple harmonies, it is another wonderful song for the early exploration of harmony.

11. Inanay Capuana

Traditional Torres Straight Islander

48

Goo - a - na goo - a - na goo - a - na goo - a - na goo - an - a___ Choo!

Goo - a - na goo - a - na goo - a - na goo - a - na goo - an - a___ Choo!

Goo - a - na goo - a - na goo - a - na goo - a - na goo - an - a___ Choo!

Goo - a - na goo - a - na goo - a - na goo - a - na goo - an - a___ Choo!

Goo - a - na goo - a - na goo - a - na goo - a - na goo - an - a___ Choo!

Goo - a - na goo - a - na goo - a - na goo - a - na goo - an - a___ Choo!

It's not so often that we get to sing a beautiful song about … a lizard. This Australian folksong, indigenous to the Torres Strait Islands, gives us the chance to do just that. *Gooana* means *lizard*, and in this song, the gooana is shooed lovingly away.

My all-time favorite version of this song is a recording an Australian friend made for me of herself singing it with her two-year-old daughter, but you can find on-line a wonderful version sung by the Australian female folk trio, Tiddas.

If you are teaching in a Waldorf school, the melody of this song can be a perfect companion for the Grade 4 study of humans in relation to animals. The harmonies can be added in later years, for example while studying Australian geography. I often add clapping or snapping on the off-beat, as you will hear in the accompanying recording.

12. Four White Horses

Jamaican Folk Song

Melody

Harmony

Four white hors - es on the riv - er, hey, hey, hey,

'up to-mor-row, 'up to-mor-row is a rain-y day. Come on and join our

shad - ow play. Shad-ow play is a ripe ba -na - na, hey, hey, hey,

'up to-mor - row, 'up to-mor - row is a rain - y day!

I learned this Caribbean children's singing game from my father and have since come across many variations and interpretations. In this version, "up tomorrow is a rainy day" is thought to mean "hope tomorrow is a rainy day." My understanding is that a rainy day would have offered the children who likely first sang this song a respite from working out in the fields.

Here's how to add the clapping:
1. Each child finds a partner and each pair finds another pair, forming groups of four.
2. Each partner stands facing her or his partner across the center, forming a cross with neighbors on either side, also facing across from partner.
3. Each child claps own hands, claps partner's hands across the center, claps own hands, then claps hands of neighbors' on either side.
4. Repeat pattern, as described in step 3, through the end of the song.
5. Each pair finds a new set of neighbors to begin again!

Since the two pairs in each group of four both clap across the center at the same time, each group has to decide which pair will clap above their neighbors first, while the other pair claps below. Then the pairs alternate clapping above and below throughout. Because the groupings keep changing with each repetition of the song, singers have the opportunity to practice quick, cooperative decision-making.

13. Fietsie Foetsie

Fiet - sie foet - sie is mijn fiet - sie. Ai, war is mijn fiet - sie?

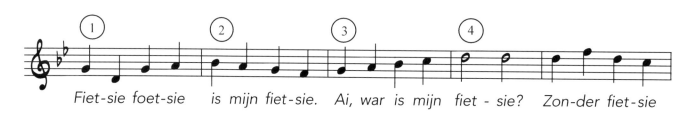

Zon - der fiet - sie kan 'k nie fiets nie. Ai, mijn fiets is foet - sie.

Fiet-sie foet-sie is mijn fiet-sie. Ai, war is mijn fiet - sie? Zon-der fiet-sie

kan 'k nie fiets nie. Ai, mijn fiets is foet - sie.

This Dutch children's song is a lament for a bicycle that's gone missing. For many years, my bicycle was my primary mode of transportation and, when it went missing one day, I was quite distraught. Years later when I learned this song, I wished I had known it at that time so I could have sung my woes away. I find that its whimsical feel combined with strong consonant sounds, stomping, and clapping makes it especially well-suited to the collective mood in Grade 4. For older children and adults as well, this song is a great way to warm up in the morning or at the beginning of a singing session. The lyrics mean:

Bicycle, my bicycle is gone.
Oh, where is my bicycle?
Without my bicycle, I can't ride.
Oh, my bicycle is gone!

14. Tue Tue

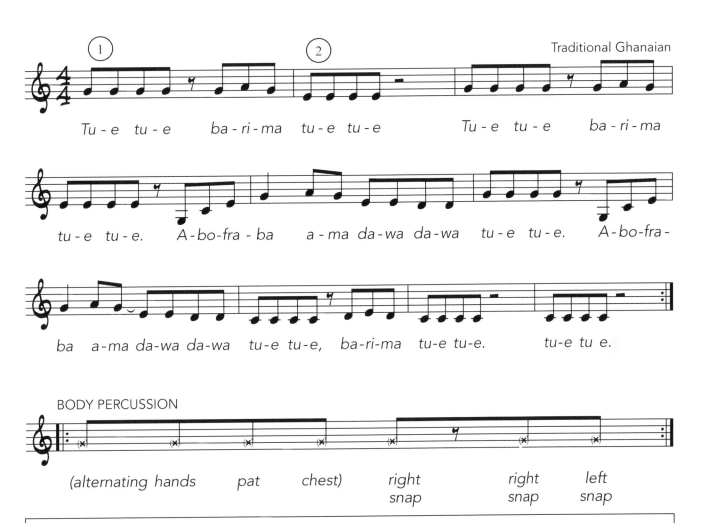

Tu - e tu - e   ba - ri - ma tu - e tu - e   Tu - e tu - e   ba - ri - ma

tu - e tu - e.   A - bo - fra - ba   a - ma da - wa da - wa tu - e tu - e.   A - bo - fra -

ba   a - ma da - wa da - wa   tu - e tu - e, ba - ri - ma   tu - e tu - e.   tu - e tu e.

BODY PERCUSSION

(alternating hands   pat   chest)   right   right   left
                                             snap   snap   snap

I first heard this folksong sung by the children of Ghanaian friends in Washington, D.C. As is the case with many folksongs, variations abound. Over the years, I've had the chance to ask several native Ghanaians about this song's origin. Many have related fond memories of singing it as a child, but none was certain of its meaning. The general consensus is that it is in the Akan language (also known as Twi) and means: "Sorry old man (barima), this small boy (abofra) accidentally tripped you and made you fall flat."

This song lends itself to the addition of body percussion. Often, the children and I make up partner clapping patterns. Alternately, we come up with a body percussion pattern that follows the rhythm of the lyrics. Then, you can alternate between just singing, singing with body percussion, and experiencing the sound of the body percussion alone. This last bit is particularly challenging and rewarding when you are working with the song as a round. I offer the song here with a simple body percussion pattern and encourage you to experiment.

15. Samba Lelê

Ba ba ba ba, Ba ba ba ba,

Ba ba ba ba, Ba ba ba ba,

ba, sam-ba ô Le - lê, Sam-ba, sam-b,a, sam-ba ô Le - lê, Sam-ba, sam-

Ba ba ba ba, Ba

Ba ba ba ba, Ba

ba, sam - ba ô Le - lê, Pi - sa na bar - ra da sa ia ô la -

Ba ba ba,___ Ba ba ba,

Ba ba ba,___ Ba ba ba,

la Sam-ba, sam-ba, sam-ba ô Co-mo é que co-zin-ha?

a - o - a,_____   a - o - a,_____   a - o - a,_____

a - o - a,_____   a - o - a,_____   a - o - a,_____

Ò   Mo - re - na bo -

a - o - a,_____   a - o - a,_____

a - o - a,_____   a - o - a,_____

ni - ta,_____   Co - mo é que co - zin - ha?_____   Bo ta a pa - ne - la no

D.S. al Coda

a - o - a,_____   Ba   ba

a - o - a,_____   Ba   ba

fo - go,_____   Vai con - ver - sar com vi - zin - ha._____

Pi - sa na bar - ra da saia ô la - la.

This lively children's song comes from Brazil. When sharing a multi-verse song in another language with native English-speakers, I often choose a single verse to sing in addition to the chorus rather than trying to tackle the entire song (unless this would distort a culturally significant meaning). Here, I've chosen the verse I find most suitable for children.

This song is greatly enhanced by the addition of body and vocal percussion. I've included some possibilities, but I encourage you to make up your own! For inspiration, check out the incredible Brazilian body percussion group, Barbatuques. Here's what the lyrics mean:

Verse:

    O, pretty brunette,
    How does one cook?
    Put the pan on the fire,
    Go and chat with the neighbor.

Chorus:

    Dance the samba, dance the samba,
    Dance the samba, o lele
    Step on the hem of the skirt, o lala.

16. Bring Me Little Water, Silvy

Composed by Lead Belly
Adapted from arrangement by Moira Smiley

Last time, ritard to end

Bring it in a buck-et, Sil - vy, Ev-ery lit-tle once in a while. __

Bring it in a buck-et, Sil - vy, Ev-ery lit-tle once in a while. __

Bring it in a buck - et, Sil - vy, hmm, Ev-ery lit-tle once in a while. __

Bring it in a buck - et, Sil - vy, hm, hm, hm, hm, Ev-ery lit-tle once in a while. __

VERSES (Sung by Soprano)

1. Sil - vy come a - run - nin' ____ buck-et in her __ hand. ___
2. Can't you see me com - in' ____ buck-et in my __ hand? ___

Back to Chorus

"I'm gon-na bring you lit - tle wa - ter ____ as fast __ as I ____ can."

"I'm gon-na bring you lit - tle wa - ter ____ as fast __ as I ____ can."

© Moira Smiley, 2007

Huddie Ledbetter, better known as Lead Belly, was one of the most powerful figures in the early years of the American folk music movement. He wrote this song about his Uncle Bob and Aunt Silvy. As the story goes, when Uncle Bob was out plowing with his mules during the hot southern summers, he would often call for Silvy to bring him some water, and the call developed into this song. This version is based on an arrangement by Moira Smiley, and I offer it with her generous permission.

This is the most harmonically complex song in this collection, and it is most appropriate for middle-school-aged children and up. You are welcome to add as many or as few of the harmony parts as best suits your group. The body percussion is also challenging, but it is the kind of challenge that adolescents in particular are ready for and generally eager to take on. Once you've mastered it, it becomes like second nature. The body percussion is taught along with the harmonies in the accompanying learning tracks for this song (visit www.singwaldorf.com, "My Harmony" to download).

17. Freedom Is Coming

Traditional South African

know.

Oh, yes I know - oh _____ oh, yes I

yes I_____ know._____ Oh, yes I know. _____ Oh,

know. Oh, _____ yes I know, oh, _____ yes I

know. Oh, _____ yes I know, oh, _____ yes I

Ritard

know.

Free-dom is com-ing, oh, yes I know.

yes I_____ know._____ Free-dom is com-ing, oh, yes I know.

know, oh,_____ yes I know, oh, yes I know.

know, oh,_____ yes I know, oh, yes I know.

This song carries with it quite a legacy. It was originally a South African church song. Anders Nyberg, a Swedish composer and peace activist, suggested changing the lyrics from "Jesus is coming" to "Freedom is coming" while leading a transformational anti-apartheid tour across South Africa in the late 1970s. Subsequently, the song took flight and became an international anthem for freedom. For some who sing it today, this song may be as much about personal liberation as it is about liberation from external constraints. For me, this song is another small way of affirming a collective commitment to working for the liberation of all people.

I first learned this song from family members who had spent time in South Africa. It arose out of a tradition rooted in improvisation and dance, and I encourage you to experiment with layering in new parts and adding rhythmic and other movement elements.

18. Nanuma

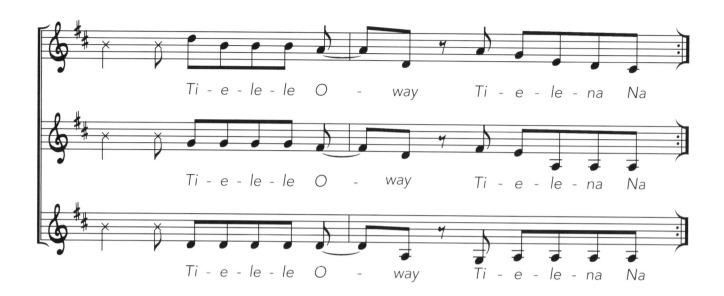

Ti - e - le - le O - way Ti - e - le - na Na

Ti - e - le - le O - way Ti - e - le - na Na

Ti - e - le - le O - way Ti - e - le - na Na

"Nanuma" found its way to me through friends many years ago. Like "Tue Tue," I've come across several versions of this song since then, and they have been attributed to various of the approximately 80 tribal languages spoken in Ghana. None of the Ghanian people I know personally recognize this particular language, though I was told it sounded like it was from northern Ghana. If you have definitive information about the origin and meaning of this song, please contact me so I can include it in future editions of this book.

The simple layering of harmonies in this song provides a fertile landscape for bringing any group into harmony. As always, you can layer in as many of the parts offered here as you wish or simply enjoy the melody. Another, simpler way of working with this song is to sing the soprano line of Part One only as a three-part round, with each new part entering along with each "Nanuma."

19. Let Your Little Light Shine

Georgia Sea Island Spiritual

I learned this spiritual from folks I sang with while living in Washington, D.C., and it has been a favorite ever since. Like "Yonder Come Day," it comes from the Georgia Sea Islands. For me, this song serves as a reminder of our responsibility toward one another and the powerful notion that, when we live from a place of courage, we uplift those around us as well as ourselves. It also invites us to consider the many layers of meaning embodied in the word "home."

The simple harmonies make it an excellent pathway into part-singing. This can be a wonderful song for Grades 4 and 5, and it lends itself to an introduction through story.

20. Come, Pretty Love

Patsy Williamson
Arranged by Meg Chittenden

Melody

Home, my pret-ty love is home,   sweet-er than the hon-ey on the comb.

Come, come, pret-ty love, come to me.   Come my pret-ty love, my hon-ey bee.

High harmony

Home, my pret-ty love is home,   sweet-er than the hon-ey on the comb.

Melody

Home, my pret-ty love is home,   sweet-er than the hon-ey on the comb.

To Coda

Come, come, pret-ty love, come to me.   Come my pret-ty love, my hon-ey bee.

Come, come, pret-ty love, come to me.   Come my pret-ty love, my hon-ey bee.

Home, my   pret-ty love is home,

Home, my   pret-ty love is home,   sweet-er than the

Come my pret-ty love, my hon-ey bee. Come, come, pret-ty love,

my hon-ey bee. Come, come, pret-ty love, come to me.

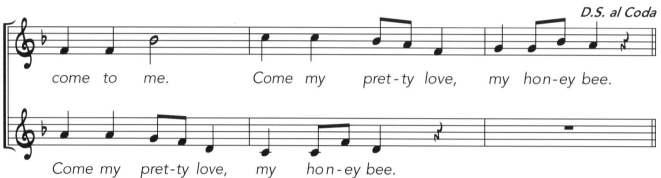

D.S. al Coda

come to me. Come my pret-ty love, my hon-ey bee.

Come my pret-ty love, my hon-ey bee.

Ritard

Come my pret-ty love, my hon-ey bee._____

Come my pret-ty love, my hon-ey bee._____

This was one of my favorite songs to sing to my daughter when she was a baby, and she loves it to this day. It is a slight adaptation of a song by Patsy Williamson, a formerly enslaved person whose freedom was purchased by the Pleasant Hill Shaker community in the early 1800s. It is said to have been a "gift" song that came to Williamson fully-formed during prayer. Like many Shaker songs and hymns, the original song celebrated the Shaker's spiritual leader, Mother Ann Lee.

In this arrangement, the song is sung in unison, then as a round, then in harmony, and finally as a round in harmony. If you are singing with children under the age of nine, sticking with the melody sung together in unison is most likely to meet them where they are. This is a wonderful song to sing as a duet, and it also works well with a group.

21. Olay La Loyla

As a teacher, I'm always looking for ways to affirm my students' natural sense of wonder. One way I've found is to start with something apparently simple and gradually unveil unexpected layers over time. Certain songs, such as this one, lend themselves especially well to this unfolding.

The lead part of this traditional Finnish herding song is fairly simple. Once you've mastered it, you can add in the harmonies. Next, try singing the lead part as a round. Then, you can add the harmonies while singing it as a round. The arrangement offered here is designed to lead you through this process. I would encourage you to take time and enjoy each phase before moving on.

One thing that gives this song a unique feel is the extra beat in the final measure of each phrase. This can make it difficult to locate the downbeat, or pulse, once you layer it into a round. Here is the method I've found most effective in enabling a group to stay with the pulse in the round:

Have all the singers bend their elbows at right angles, palms facing down. Keeping elbows still, mark the beat with a steady downward motion, as if patting down the air. The first time through, the downward motion will be on the first and third beat of the measure, or all of the "O"s and the "loy"s for the first three lines. The fourth line is offset, but if you maintain that steady pulse with your hands, you will land with a down motion on the final "la" of that phrase. The syllables that coincide with the downward motion the first time through are in bold below. (Note that in the last line, one of the down motions comes between two syllables and is written as "down"):

O lay la **loy**-la, **O** lay la **loy**-la, **O** lay la **loy**-la, **O** **lay** o lay (**down**) la loy-**la**.

If you continue to keep this steady pulse, then the second time through the song, it will feel like you're marking the pulse on the off-beat, or when your hands are up instead of down. To emphasize this shift, I have singers turn their palms face up at this point, as if pushing the air into the shoulders instead of down towards the ground. Now, the hands will come up on all of the syllables in bold above.

On the third time through the song, if you keep that same steady beat, the pulse will align with the downward motion again, just as in the first time through. Here, the singers turn their palms to face down again to help them feel the return to the downward pulse.

To sum up, singers keep a steady, unwavering pulse throughout the song by moving their hands up and down with each beat. The first time through, palms face down, the second time through, palms face up, and so on, alternating with each repetition through the completion of the song. Good luck!

22. Sana Lwam

Traditional Xhosa

This traditional Xhosa song was taught to me by South African singer and activist, Sharon Katz, of Sharon Katz & The Peace Train. Her recording and arrangement can be found on the album Imbizo and also on Putumayo's *Kids World Music Dance Party*. More information about Sharon, her music, and her work for peace and justice can be found at www.SharonKatz.com.

This song is sung from the perspective of a parent singing to his or her child and means: "Baby (*sana*) of mine (*lwam*), I am proud of you. I will carry you on my back, even while you are sleeping." My understanding is that it is still often sung at Xhosa weddings in South Africa. It can be a great song for bringing a large group together in song, particularly with the addition of percussion and movement.

23. Hosay Yaa

Traditional Ewe of Ghana

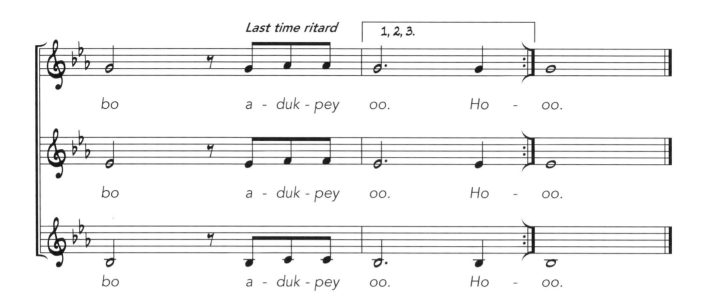

bo ... a - duk - pey oo. Ho - oo.

bo ... a - duk - pey oo. Ho - oo.

bo ... a - duk - pey oo. Ho - oo.

With its simple, parallel harmonies, "Hosay Yaa" is a wonderful song for introducing part-singing. It comes from the Gahu tradition of the Ewe people of West Africa, who live primarily in Ghana and Togo. The Gahu tradition is a form of music and dance that arose out of a Yoruban style of music from Nigeria that later took root in Ghana. It is seen as music for all people, with no specific religious or spiritual connotations.

I understand this to be a song sung in gratitude to our mothers and the older women in our lives who nurture and protect us. In the Ewe language, hosay is a greeting, and yaa refers to a woman born on Thursday, while maame means "mother" or "madam." The second part of the text is Yoruba (Nigerian), and in this language, adukpey means "thank you" and ekabo means "you're welcome."

24. Elk Herd Song

Unknown

Soprano
1. Eve - ning finds the elk herd de - part - ing
2. Bow - ing low, they drink the crys - tal wa - ters,

Alto
1. Eve - ning finds the elk herd de - part - ing
2. Bow - ing low, they drink the crys - tal wa - ters,

Bass
1. Eve - ning finds the elk ___ herd de - part - ing
2. Bow - ing low, they drink the crys - tal wa - ters,

from the dunes and lake - side ___ sands.
stars re - flect - ing like the heavens a - bove.

from the dunes and lake - side ___ sands.
stars re - flect - ing like the heavens a - bove.

from the dunes and lake - side sands.
stars re - flect - ing like the heavens a - bove.

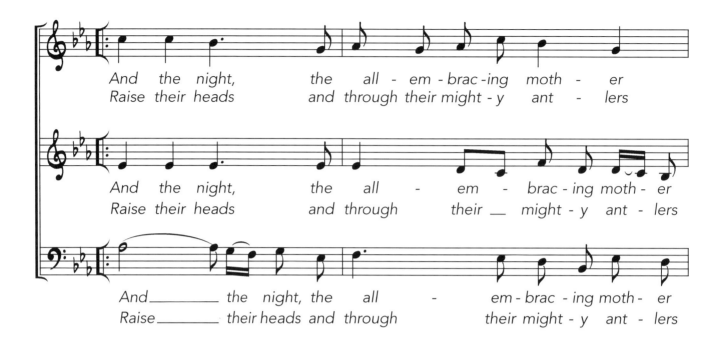

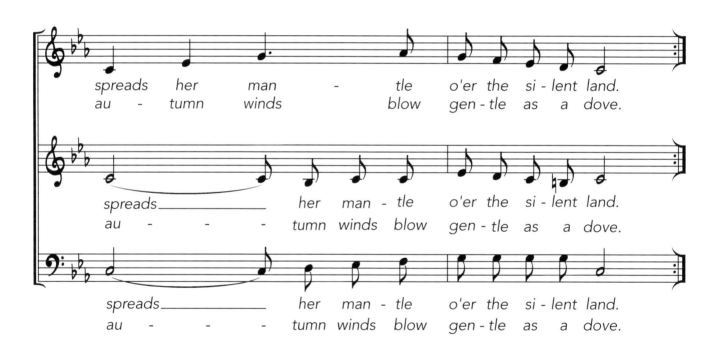

3. Silently, they leave the misty shores then,
   Remnants of a long forgotten day.
   And they vanish in the distant spaces,
   Through the portal of eternity.

While I have yet to discover the exact origin of this beautiful song, it is in the style of European composers who traveled to North America in the early 1800s and found inspiration in the vastness of the countryside and the indigenous music of its people.

The beauty that arises from bringing these harmonies together is well worth the effort, though the complexity makes this song most appropriate for middle-school-aged children and up.

There are so many ways to enrich and enliven the experience of singing together. For example, one 8th grade class and I created a large-scale crankie, or scrolling story, to accompany this song. If you would like to witness this enchanting medium in action, visit www.singwaldorf.com or google "elk herd crankie." I hope it will inspire you to make crankies of your own!

25. Yemaya

Traditional Yoruba

In the Yoruba religion, which arose out of Nigeria and Benin, an *orisha* is a kind of mediator between human beings and the spiritual realm. Yemaya, or Yemoja, is the orisha most connected with water and the nurturing feminine. Her name comes from "Yeye omo eja" which means, "Mother whose children are like fish."

For me, this song is an opportunity to reflect on the life-giving, all-encompassing presence of the watery element in ourselves and in our world. Traditionally, this song was probably sung in unison, perhaps with improvised harmonies. It can also be sung as a round or in harmony, as it is presented here.

What'll I Do with the Baby-O?

Wrap him up in cal - i - co, Wrap him up in cal - i - co.

Wrap him up in cal - i - co, Wrap him up in cal - i - co.

Wrap him up in cal - i - co, Wrap him up in cal - i - co.

2. Dance her North and dance her South,
   Dance her North and dance her South,
   Dance her North and dance her South,
   Dance her North and dance her South.

3. Hang him up in the tall tree top,
   Hang him up in the tall tree top,
   Hang him up in the tall tree top,
   The wind will blow and the cradle
   will rock.

FINAL CHORUS:
That's what I'll do with the baby-o,
That's what I'll do with the baby-o,
That's what I'll do with the baby-o,
If he won't go to sleepy-o.
(Repeat)

The sentiment expressed by this traditional Appalachian folksong is likely to resonate with anyone who's been a primary care-giver for a baby. I learned it from my father and sang it to my own children when they were babies. Now, I often catch them singing it to one of their stuffed animals or dolls as they tuck it into bed.

As always, if singing this song with children under age nine, I encourage you to simply sing the melody. Young children often enjoy making up motions together with you to accompany singing this song. With older children and adults, the harmonies are a wonderful addition.

27. Evening Rise

Unknown

Eve - ning rise, spir - it __ come. Sun goes down when the

Eve - ning rise, spir - it come. Sun goes down when the

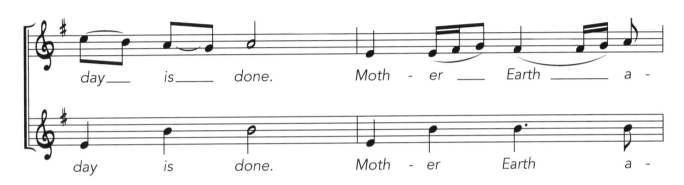

day __ is __ done. Moth - er __ Earth __ a -

day is done. Moth - er Earth a -

1, 2.

wak - ens __ me with the heart - beat of the __ sea.

wak - ens me with the heart - beat of the __ sea.

Last time

sea, with the heart - beat __ of the __ sea.

sea, with the heart - beat of the __ sea.

Like "The Elk Herd," I believe this song arose out of the stream of European music inspired by relatively early contact with North America. This song's single harmony can serve as an excellent bridge from simple, parallel harmonies into more complex part-singing. When I teach this song, I have all singers learn both parts and switch back and forth to increase flexibility and capacity to hold a part while tuning into the whole.

28. Little Birch Tree

Traditional Russian

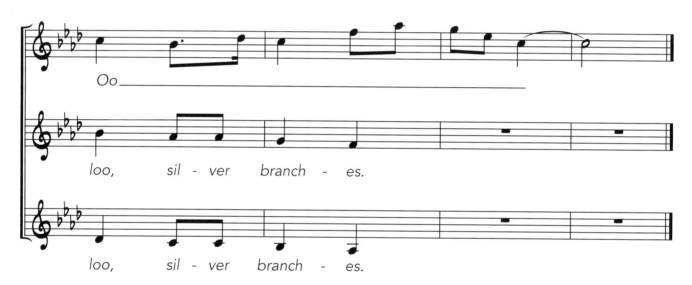

3. From a branch I'll carve a balalaika.
   With the flutes I'll play my balalaika.
   Loo-li-loo, balalaika,
   Loo-li-loo, balalaika.

4. When I play my tinkling balalaika,
   I'll remember you, my little birch tree.
   Loo-li-loo, little birch tree,
   Loo-li-loo little birch tree.

Birch trees were regarded with great reverence in the ancient culture of central Russia, out of which this song arose. The birch was a symbol of Spring and was considered to hold powers of protection. The Russian word for birch, *bereza*, is associated with the verb for "to keep, to take care," and birch trees were often planted surrounding a village to ward off sickness and harm.

Children around the age of nine tend to love the melancholy mood of this song, though they are not yet ready to sing the harmony. If you are a teacher with the opportunity to work with multiple grades, you may wish to consider teaching the harmony to older children and then bringing them together with the younger group. Teaching a song across grades can give the younger children a little glimpse of where they are headed musically, while providing older students with the chance to offer their advanced skill in service to the younger ones. Meanwhile, everyone involved has the unifying and uplifting experience of creating beautiful music together.

29. Little Red Bird

Traditional Manx

U - shag veg ruy ny moa - nee doo, moa - nee doo, moa - nee doo, U - shag veg ruy ny moa - nee doo, C'raad cha - ddil oo riyr syn oie?

Oo_____ Oo_____

Lit - tle red bird on the lone - ly moor, lone - ly moor,

Oo_____ Oo_____

lone - ly moor, Lit - tle red bird on the lone - ly moor,

Oo where did you sleep in the night?

VERSES

Melody 1.Out on the bare branch dark and wide, dark and wide,

Low descant Oo Oo

dark and wide. Fast the rain fell on ev' - ry side.

Oo

1, 2, 3.

Poor was my sleep in the night.

Oo

High descant

Oo_____

Melody

Sweet   was   my   sleep   in   the   night._____

Low descant

Oo_____

2. Did I not sleep on a swaying briar,
Swaying briar, swaying briar?
Tossed all about as the wind rose higher,
Poor was my sleep in the night.

3. Did I not sleep on a cold wave's crest,
Cold wave's crest, cold wave's crest,
  Where many a man has taken his rest,
  Poor was my sleep in the night.

4. Wrapped in two leaves I lay at ease,
Lay at ease, lay at ease,
As sleeps the young babe on his
    mother's knees,
Sweet was my sleep in the night.

This hauntingly beautiful Manx lullaby is another song that lends itself particularly well to introduction through story. It can be quite lovely to tell the story just as it unfolds in the song. Sometimes, especially around Christmas, I add that the little red bird is journeying towards a distant place where a special child has just been born. Though the bird must spend each night in great discomfort, he presses on. At last, he reaches the warm cave filled with the light of the newborn babe. There, he sings for the baby and its mother and spends that night snug among soft leaves that have opened, as if by some miracle, on a bush at the mouth of the cave, despite the chill of winter.

The element of harmony in this arrangement is brought through the addition of a high and low descant. The interplay of these harmonies reinforces the sense of two voices, one that asks and the other, the voice of the bird himself, that replies. Both the mood and the imagery of this song seem to resonate especially deeply with children around the age of nine. The harmonies are best saved for older children and adults.

30. Mo Li Hua

Traditional Chinese

Melody

Hao yi duo mei - li de mò li___ hua.

Harmony

Hao yi duo mei - li de

Fen-fang mei - li___ man zhi - ya. Yòu xiang yòu bái

mò li___ hua. Fen-fang mei - li___ man zhi - ya. Yòu yòu

rén rén ai. Ráng wo___ lái jiang ni zhai xiá.

rén rén ai. Ráng wo___ lái jiang

Sòng gei bie rén jia mò li hua ya mò li___ hua.

ni zhai xiá. mò li hua ya mò li hua.

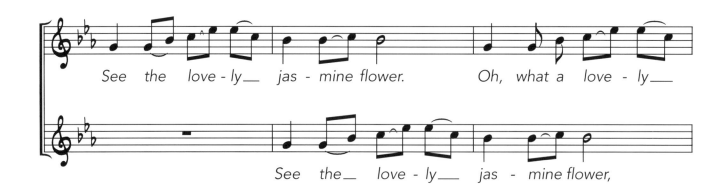

See the love-ly__ jas-mine flower. Oh, what a love-ly__

See the__ love-ly__ jas-mine flower,

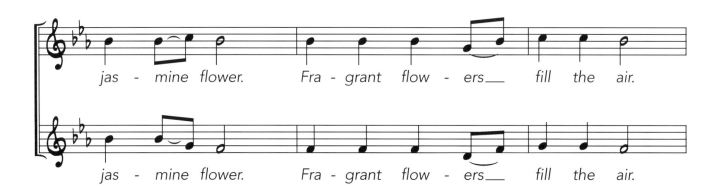

jas-mine flower. Fra-grant flow-ers__ fill the air.

jas-mine flower. Fra-grant flow-ers__ fill the air.

Beau-ti-ful blos-soms ev-'ry-where. Choose a__ blos-som

Beau-ty ev-'ry-where.

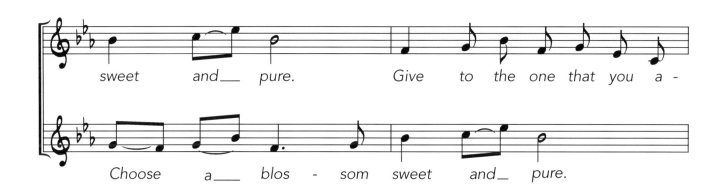

sweet and__ pure. Give to the one that you a-

Choose a__ blos-som sweet and__ pure.

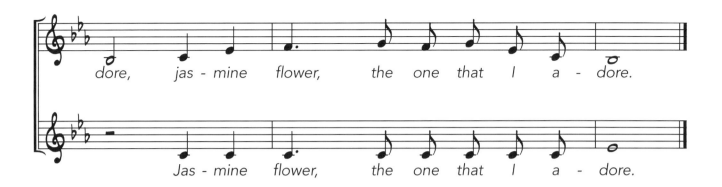

"Mo Li Hua" is probably the Chinese folksong most well-known outside of China. Dating back to the 18th Century, it has played a varied role within Chinese culture and history. Once serving as a temporary national anthem by Qing officials while visiting Europe, it was more recently associated with the 2011 Jasmine Revolution, when pro-democracy protesters used it as a symbol of anti-government solidarity.

The pentatonic melody is appropriate for even very young children. The harmony can be added with older children, ages ten and up. Because both parts are in a medium range, it is a nice song for introducing more complex, non-parallel part-singing to early middle-school-aged children whose voices have not yet begun to change.

Here are the lyrics written in their original language:

好一朵美麗的茉莉花
好一朵美麗的茉莉花
芬芳美麗滿枝椏
又香又白人人誇
讓我來將你摘下
送給別人家
茉莉花呀茉莉花

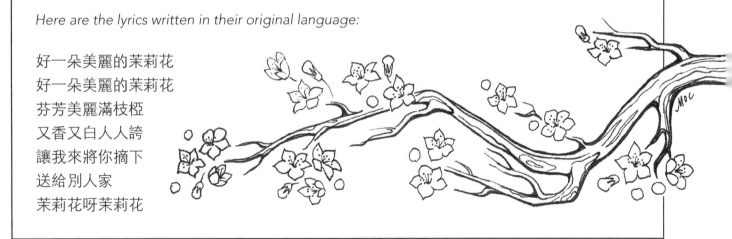

31. Deep Peace

William Sharp (a.k.a Fiona Macleod)

1. Deep peace of the run-ning wave to you.

2. Deep peace of the flow-ing air to you.

3. Deep peace of the shin-ing stars to you.

4. Deep peace of the qui-et Earth to you.

This blessing, often attributed to ancient Gaelic sources, was actually written in the late 1800s by Scottish poet, William Sharp, under his alternate literary identity, Fiona Macleod. The full blessing can be found in Dominion of Dreams under a Dark Star (1895). In the version offered here, the text has been set to a melody that creates beautiful harmonies when sung as a round.

Through both its melody and imagery, this song conveys a sense of balance – between above and below, earth and sky, water and air. This makes it particularly well-suited for children around the age of ten (Grade 5), who stand in the balance between childhood and adolescence. The range is substantial; one of the wonderful things about singing in a group is that you can always drop out on the highest and/or lowest notes and let others carry those. As mentioned in "A Note for Parents and Teachers," I err on the side of fewer parts sung with greater accuracy rather than the opposite. While this round can be sung in four parts, if it is a stretch for your group to sing all four parts with confidence, it is so much more powerful to sing just two parts with clarity and purity of pitch.

32. Russian Lullaby

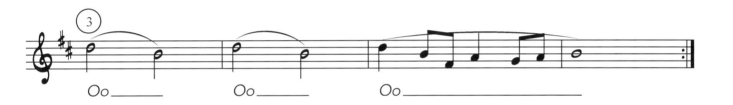

The quiet beauty of this traditional Russian lullaby seemed a fitting way to bring this collection to a close. With its somewhat melancholy mood and minor key, it is most appropriate to sing with ages nine and up. I find that it resonates particularly well as a round when children have reached early adolescence. Over the years in our school, this song has found its way into various class plays and been a lovely addition to our Winter concert as well. It is a beautiful way to welcome in the night. There is a wonderful version of this song on Libana's album, *A Circle Is Cast*.

When I introduce a song in this style sung on the syllable "oo," I encourage students to keep the front of the face lifted and the inside of the mouth as open as possible to ensure that the sound is clear, round, and full.

May your days be filled with light, and may each give way harmoniously into night!

Resources

Association of Waldorf Schools of North America (ASWNA): www.waldorfeducation.org
Through AWSNA, you can connect with information about Waldorf education, specific
    schools and employment opportunities, and a range of additional Waldorf resources
    and publications.

Association for Waldorf Music Education: www. waldorfmusic.org
AWME provides a forum for the sharing of resources, colleagueship, and conversation
    towards supporting and strengthening the presence of music in the education of
    the whole child.

Waldorf School Songs: www.waldorfschoolsongs.com
Through this website, Dutch Waldorf teacher, Matthijs Overmars, and his fellow editors offer
    a searchable treasure trove of over 1000 songs commonly sung in Waldorf schools.

Music through the Grades by Diane Ingraham Barnes
A wonderful teacher resource including over 200 songs arranged seasonally and offered "in
    the light of the developing child," spanning Grades 1–8. Available through www.
    florisbooks.org

MUSIC FOR YOUNG CHILDREN

This collection is intended primarily for singers ages nine and up. Here are some of my
    favorite music resources for early childhood:

Naturally You Can Sing: www.naturallyyoucansing.com
Naturally You Can Sing is the source of the full collection of beautiful songbooks for
    young children created by Mary Thinness Schunemann. They offer a range of
    additional books and resources to support you in creating a nurturing environment
    in your home.

Books by Wilma Ellersiek
Wilma Ellersiek offers several rich and nourishing collections of seasonal songs and gesture
    games for very young children. Available through Floris Books, www.florisbooks.org

A Lifetime of Joy by Bronja Zahlingen

A wonderful collection of circle games, finger games, songs, verses, and plays for puppets and marionettes collected, created, adapted and translated by Bronja Zahlingen. This is perhaps my all-time favorite resource for early childhood. Available through Waldorf Publications, www.waldorfpublications.org

I Love to Be Me: Songs in the Mood of the Fifth by Channa Seidenberg

A beautifully-illustrated selection of thirty-two songs composed especially for young children. Available through Steiner Books, www.steinerbooks.org

A Word of Thanks

I would like to express my heartfelt thanks to…

All of the GIFTED COMPOSERS who created the songs offered here and the friends, teachers, and kin who passed them on to me.

PATRICE MAYNARD and WALDORF PUBLICATIONS for working with me to bring this project to life.

All of the fine folks who contributed to the crowdfunding campaign that made this project possible. A special thanks to WILLIAM ALTMAN, who produced our video, and all of the lovely people from our community who participated in its creation.

KIM PERALTA of Saltfield Farm, who offered her space, equipment, and expertise to get me started in recording these songs for you.

My father, PAUL KELLY, a musician and teacher, who, in addition to being a fantastically supportive father and grandfather, did the bulk of the work to generate the sheet music offered in this collection.

My aunt, REVEREND CAROL KELLY, an experienced Waldorf teacher and Antioch faculty member, who taught me many of my favorite songs, including several offered here, and continues to be a primary mentor for me in music, Waldorf education, and life in general.

IAN CHITTENDEN, who, in addition to being a Waldorf alum and veteran Waldorf class teacher, is also my husband, life-partner, trusted support and primary collaborator, the builder of our home, the tender of our garden, and the loving father of our two growing children.

Our children, CLANCY (6) and CELIA (4), who inspire, motivate, and guide me, and who support this work by always being ready to join in the song!

And finally, I offer my thanks to you for having the courage and optimism to lift your voice in song!

Made in the USA
Middletown, DE
25 June 2017